This book
belongs to

....

ISBN: 978-1-7365471-0-6 (Paperback)
ISBN: 978-1-7365471-1-3 (eBook)
ISBN: 978-1-7365471-2-0 (Hardcover)

To the shelters and rescue organizations that work tirelessly to save the underdogs.

To fosters and volunteers who offer their time, homes and hearts.

And to the adopters who give secondhand dogs a new leash on life.

To our rescue dog, Sofie, who taught me to be a proud dog Mom!

To Last Hope K9 Recue that brought her to us and forever changed our lives.

And in loving memory of my first dog, Astra, who ignited my love and passion for dogs.

Hello! I am Sofie. I am a pure mutt.
I don't have pedigree. I am not a pure breed; so what!
I am spunky and loyal; I have a lot of zest.
My friends' gloomy fate has inspired my quest:

No matter how old you are, let's unite!
We need to support fairness, respect and the underdog fight.

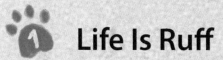

Life Is Ruff

"Rescue does not mean 'damaged'.
It means these dogs have been let down by humans."

I was lucky that my pregnant mother was found
After her owner abandoned her at the rescue pound.
My ten siblings and I could have died.
Instead, we are curious about what life will provide.

It appears that my new friends here also need to adjust.
My friends have come to the shelter, just like the rest of us,
Because of other people's doing and no fault of their own.
They were no longer wanted and are scared of the unknown.

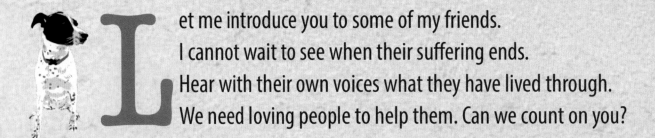

L et me introduce you to some of my friends.
I cannot wait to see when their suffering ends.
Hear with their own voices what they have lived through.
We need loving people to help them. Can we count on you?

"Hi, I'm Milo, a Pointer. I was let go without reason
At the end of the annual duck hunting season.
It costs too much to care for me and it became clear.
It is much cheaper to get a new puppy next year."

"Hello, I am Kenzie, a Dalmatian. My body is tired.
I was used for breeding until I was finally retired.
I bore many puppies, one after the other.
I can no longer give birth or care as a mother."

"My name is Rex, a Shepherd. I was very unlucky.
I was getting too old and was replaced with a puppy.
My owner wanted to escape my age and my dysplasia.
Now, the staff works on my adoption to avoid my euthanasia."

The shelter staff treats us all very well.
They don't care about our age and they do not yell.
They clean our kennels and they love us to pieces.
They work very hard, so the number of adoptions increases.

"Hi, I'm Joy, a Labradoodle. I need extensive grooming.
Breeders sell expensive Doodles. Their businesses are booming.
Despite Doodles being mutts, people buy us as "designer" pets.
Later, high grooming and vet bills often cause regrets."

"Hi, I'm Fred, a Beagle. My owner moved to an elderly home.
I also had to move since I could not stay alone.
Both my Daddy and I are still in mourning.
Our perfect life together ended without much warning."

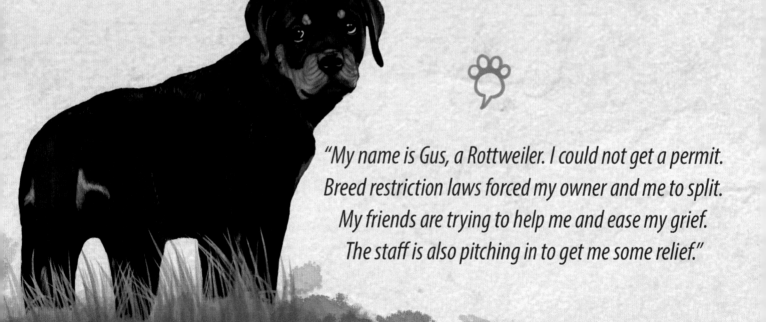

"My name is Gus, a Rottweiler. I could not get a permit.
Breed restriction laws forced my owner and me to split.
My friends are trying to help me and ease my grief.
The staff is also pitching in to get me some relief."

My friends and I look forward to when the volunteers arrive.
We know it will be playtime and we all can revive.
They take us for walks and we play with balls.
It is nice to go outside beyond the shelter walls.

*"Hello, I am Lola, a slim Greyhound. I had fended
For myself for weeks when Greyhound racing ended.
I fought for survival and fortunately, I was found.
I am grateful that I am here now at the rescue pound."*

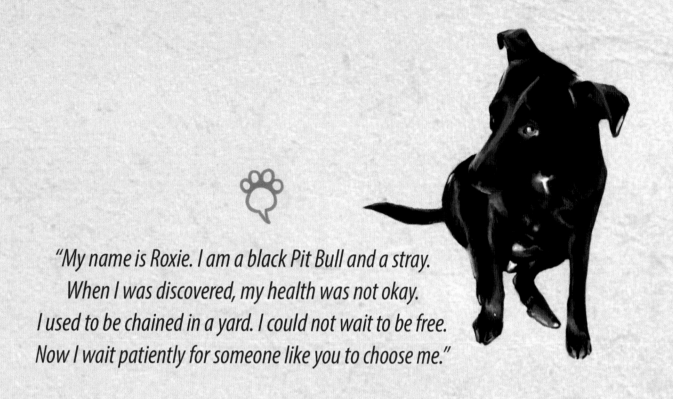

"My name is Roxie. I am a black Pit Bull and a stray.
When I was discovered, my health was not okay.
I used to be chained in a yard. I could not wait to be free.
Now I wait patiently for someone like you to choose me."

I can continue to tell more stories if you allow.
But I am sure that you understand my message now.
I am happy you are interested and you ask, "How can I help you?"
Please support us to ease what our dogs have to go through.

If your family owns pets, please treat them with respect.
They deserve your love and care. It is our duty to protect.
Please also help us to educate on neuter and on spay.
There are already too many puppies on this earth today.

Did you know that many dogs that come to our pound
Are stray dogs who have run away and luckily are found.
Microchips increase success to reunite owners and their pets.
Please help us raise awareness, so there are no regrets.

My name is Sofie. I am a pure mutt.
I don't have pedigree. I am not a pure breed; so what!
I am spunky and loyal; I have a lot of zest.
My friends' gloomy fate has inspired my quest:

No matter how old you are, let's unite!
We need to support fairness, respect and the underdog fight.

DID YOU KNOW ?

There are more than 10,000 puppy mills in the United States.

Every 60 seconds, one animal suffers abuse. Close to 65% of all abused animals are dogs and 25% of all abused dogs are Pit Bulls.

Approx. 3.3 million dogs enter United States animal shelters every year. 67% are animals found on the street. Microchipping increases the return rate of lost dogs by 250%.

The overpopulation of dogs is a major problem in the US. Only 10% of animals entering shelters have been spayed or neutered. One unspayed dog and her puppies can produce 67,000 dogs in just 6 years.

Rescue Is My Favorite Breed

"Saving one dog will not change the world, but surely for that dog, the world will change forever."

All of us here wait patiently for our future place.
But we do need to hurry. It is indeed a race.
The kennel space is limited and more dogs arrive.
The situation is serious. It is not clear who will survive.

The shelters in the South don't have sufficient adoptions.
Therefore, we need urgently to explore alternative options.
Rescue organizations work hard to move us out of state.
They are determined to increase our low adoption rate.

Rescues match us with foster homes to prepare us really well.
They get us out of the shelter and help us to excel.
Fosters love us like their own. They see our potential.
They commit and fight for us. This is extremely essential.

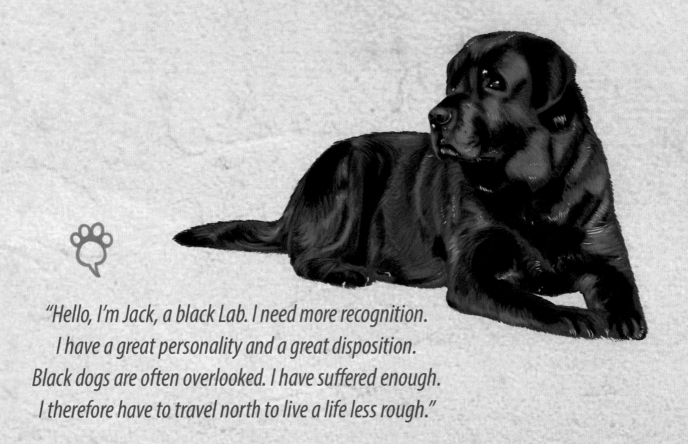

Let me introduce you to some more of my friends.
I cannot wait to see when their suffering ends.
Hear from them how much rescue organizations do.
Rescue always needs more people. Can we count on you?

"Hello, I'm Jack, a black Lab. I need more recognition.
I have a great personality and a great disposition.
Black dogs are often overlooked. I have suffered enough.
I therefore have to travel north to live a life less rough."

"Hi I'm Lottie, a Shar Pei. My skin disease has improved.
My owners left me alone in an empty house when they moved.
My fosters provided special care. I am beautiful today.
I now have so much energy. I always love to play."

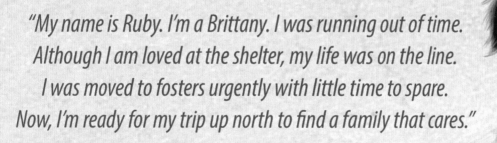

"My name is Ruby. I'm a Brittany. I was running out of time.
Although I am loved at the shelter, my life was on the line.
I was moved to fosters urgently with little time to spare.
Now, I'm ready for my trip up north to find a family that cares."

Rescues work free for us. This is something that is rare.
They provide surgery, medicine, and tender loving care.
They treat illness, vaccinate, and also neuter or spay.
They make sure we are strong enough before we're on our way.

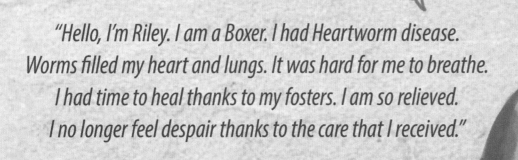

"Hello, I'm Riley. I am a Boxer. I had Heartworm disease.
Worms filled my heart and lungs. It was hard for me to breathe.
I had time to heal thanks to my fosters. I am so relieved.
I no longer feel despair thanks to the care that I received."

"My name is Maggie. I'm a Tripod. I was thrown out of a car.
I had many broken bones. I also have many scars.
Due to nurturing fosters, I am healthy and I'm still trusting.
I run fast despite my missing leg and will need little adjusting."

M

any puppies like me would suffer and die,
If fosters did not care for us and would not try
To Prevent Parvo, often a deadly disease,
Treat parasites and blood sucking ticks and fleas.

"Hi again, Roxie here! I'm a Pit Bull. I cannot live in this state.
I need to be adopted outside to have a better fate.
Pit bulls aren't appreciated and are often even feared.
I am working extra hard for prejudices to disappear. "

I can continue to tell more stories if you allow.
But I am sure that you understand my message now.
I am happy you are interested and you ask, "How can I help you?"
Please support us to ease what our dogs have to go through.

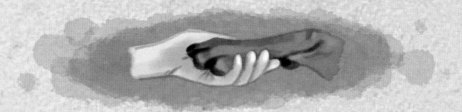

Shelters would love your help, if you have time to spare.

Be a volunteer and support the staff with daily animal care.

If your family can foster, more dogs will stay alive.

It will be hard to say goodbye, but so worth it when dogs survive.

Support us by educating and spreading our important story.

Rescues need financial help, so that they don't need to worry.

Also, help us advocate against prejudice and unfairness.

Certain breeds are singled out. We need to create awareness.

My name is Sofie. I am a pure mutt.
I don't have pedigree. I am not a pure breed; so what!
I am spunky and loyal; I have a lot of zest.
My friends' gloomy fate has inspired my quest:

No matter how old you are, let's unite!
We need to support fairness, respect and the underdog fight.

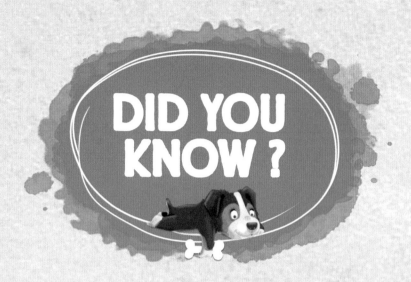

DID YOU KNOW ?

There are an estimated 14,000 shelters and rescue groups in the United States.

In 2019, 625,000 pets were euthanized because shelters were too full and there were not enough adoptive homes. But there is good news! The number of pets being euthanized has dropped from 17 million in 1984 and 2019 was the second consecutive year the number was below 1 million

Pit Bulls, which make up 93% of shelter dogs, have the highest euthanasia rate. Only 1 in 600 pit bulls will be adopted. A temperament test by the American Temperament Testing Society showed that Pit Bulls are slightly less aggressive than Golden Retrievers.

3 Finding a Fur-Ever Home

"You can't change a dog's past, but you can rewrite his future!"

Come by the shelter to meet us, but be aware
We need different types of homes. It is only fair
That you understand our needs; that you know what to expect.
We're long-term commitments. Choose wisely who you select.

You save two lives – your dog's and the space you create for another.
You and your pup will be lucky to have found each other.
Once you win your new dog's trust, its love and its affection.
You will gain a loyal companion, a guard for your protection.

Let me introduce you to some more of my friends.
I cannot wait to see when their suffering ends.
Hear with their own voices what kind of homes would be best.
Let's educate potential adopters. Will you help with our request?

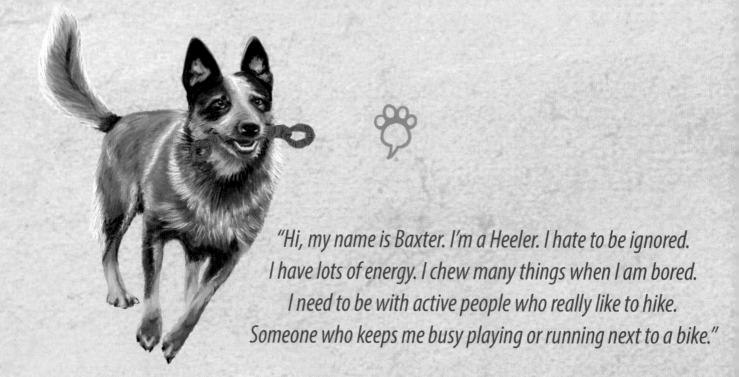

"Hi, my name is Baxter. I'm a Heeler. I hate to be ignored.
I have lots of energy. I chew many things when I am bored.
I need to be with active people who really like to hike.
Someone who keeps me busy playing or running next to a bike."

"Hello, I'm Sadie, I'm a Setter. I am now elderly and blind.
I am not very energetic. I am quiet. I am kind.
I like a comfortable couch or an "old dog retreat".
I need to feel safe. I cannot live on a busy street."

"Hello, I'm Finn, a Leonberger. I'm calm and I listen well.
I am a gentle giant. I start to come out of my shell.
I love children, other dogs, and I even like the cat.
I need sufficient space and not only a small flat."

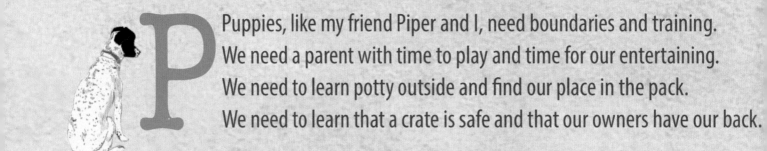

P Puppies, like my friend Piper and I, need boundaries and training.
We need a parent with time to play and time for our entertaining.
We need to learn potty outside and find our place in the pack.
We need to learn that a crate is safe and that our owners have our back.

"Hi, we are Belle & Max, two Chihuahuas. We're a bonded pair.
Please adopt us together. We each like to share.
We cannot be apart. We need each other to live in peace.
If we are separated, our fears and anxiety will increase."

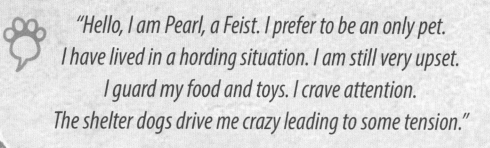

"Hello, I am Pearl, a Feist. I prefer to be an only pet.
I have lived in a hording situation. I am still very upset.
I guard my food and toys. I crave attention.
The shelter dogs drive me crazy leading to some tension."

"Hello, I'm Cooper, a Ridgeback. I am skin and bone.
I am a bit of a loner. My owner left me outside alone.
Give me time to warm up. Gain my trust with toys.
I need to be in a home with not too much noise."

"My name is Rosie. I am a Foxhound. I love to please.
I am lovable and sparky. I love when you tease.
I need to be with older children as I like to bounce.
I am easily corrected and I will learn quickly, no doubt."

"Hello, I'm Enzo, a French Bulldog. I am gasping for air.
My snout is too short. So, please be aware.
This can cause high medical costs, a life full of pain.
It's crucial you know this, so that you won't return me again."

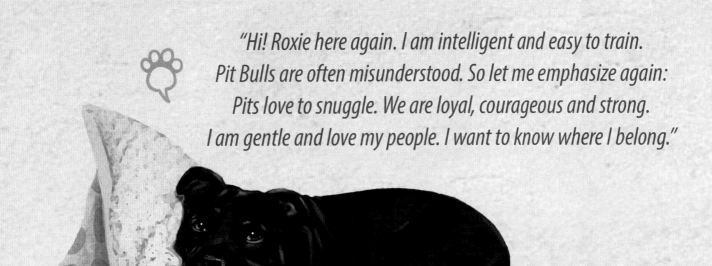

"Hi! Roxie here again. I am intelligent and easy to train.
Pit Bulls are often misunderstood. So let me emphasize again:
Pits love to snuggle. We are loyal, courageous and strong.
I am gentle and love my people. I want to know where I belong."

I can continue to tell more stories if you allow.
But I am sure that you understand my message now.
I am happy you are interested and you ask, "How can I help you?"
Please support us to ease what our dogs have to go through.

Many young and healthy dogs look for a suitable home.
Please help us spread this message. We cannot save them alone.
There are not only mutts; there are also pure breeds.
Adopters can find one that fulfills their needs.

Rescue dogs are cheaper. Their personality is known.
Fosters raised and trained them as if they were their own.
If more people adopt from rescues, more dogs will stay alive.
We need to educate potential adopters, so that more survive.

My name is Sofie. I am a pure mutt.
I don't have pedigree. I am not a pure breed; so what!
I am spunky and loyal; I have a lot of zest.
My friends' gloomy fate has inspired my quest:

No matter how old you are, let's unite!
We need to support fairness, respect and the underdog fight.

DID YOU KNOW ?

 99% of shelter animals are healthy and adoptable. The average age of shelter dogs is under 18 months old and 25% are purebred.

 23% of dogs are adopted from rescue organizations, while 34% of dogs are purchased from breeders. Other dog sources are relatives, friends or found as strays.

 Reasons to adopt from a shelter

- You save two lives - the dog you adopt and the shelter space you create for another dog

- You have a better chance of knowing the animal's personality

- Shelters offer more options

- Shelters are less expensive and a good value

Anything Is Paws-ible

"Rescue - It's not a verb, it's a promise."

Roxie, my siblings and I, we are lucky ones.
We got out of the shelter. We found fosters and permanent homes.
We are loved and spoiled. Our families take good care.
Luckily, before they adopted us, they took time to prepare.

Do you know what dogs need to be healthy, safe and happy?
They need a home with someone who cares that they don't feel crappy.
They need water, food, exercise, playtime, and attention.
They need to be part of a pack. They need vet visits for prevention.

When you bring us rescues home, the work is just beginning.
Consider the "Rule of 3". If you do, we will both be winning.
For 3 days, we try to figure things out. After 3 weeks, we start a routine.
It takes us 3 months to become part of your family. Give us time to settle in.

Let me introduce you to some more of my friends.
I am so happy that their suffering now finally ends.
Hear from them what kind of activities bring them joy.
Spend time with your dog. You will love it. Enjoy!

"Hi! I'm Axel, a Doberman. Now I'm a companion pet.
My Dad was in the military. When he came home, he was very upset.
Black dogs are often overlooked. But I am going to shine.
I am supporting my Dad emotionally. My future will be fine."

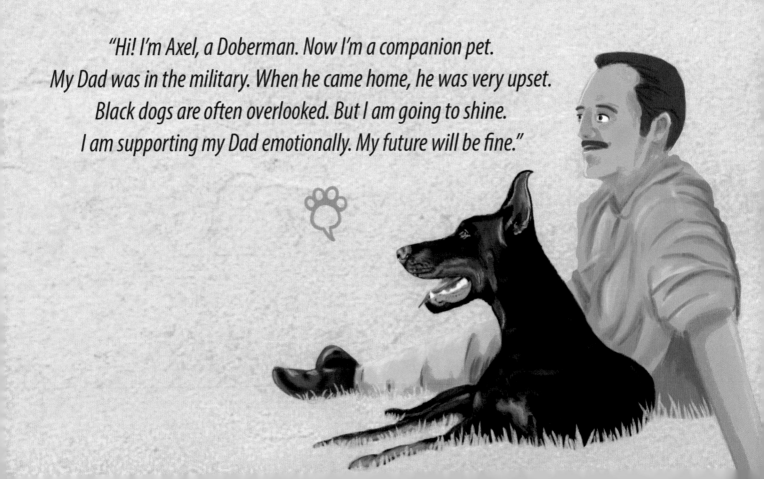

"My name is Coco, I'm a Poodle. I am a therapy pet.
I am visiting hospitals. I am helping children forget.
I provide affection and comfort. I got my permit.
I had to pass several tests before I became legit."

"Hi! I'm Bruno, a Bloodhound. I have a strong sense of smell.
I am loyal and calm. I can detect when you're not well.
I am trained as a service dog. I have one major goal.
I will smell when your blood sugar is out of control."

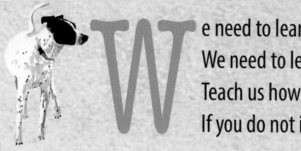

We need to learn what you want from us; e.g., to "sit" or "stay".
We need to learn a crate is safe for the time when you are away.
Teach us how to potty outside. Please make the effort to train.
If you do not invest sufficient time, please do not complain.

"My name is Ally. I'm a mongrel, also known as a mutt.
I am such a good girl. I cannot stop wiggling my butt.
Dad and I completed the "Canine Good Citizen" test.
Mom is very proud of us. My cat brother is impressed."

"Hello! I am Kira. I am a Sheltie. I love agility.
I run like the wind. I have special mobility.
I race through the tunnel. I love to weave around the poles.
We are a great team together. We know our specific roles."

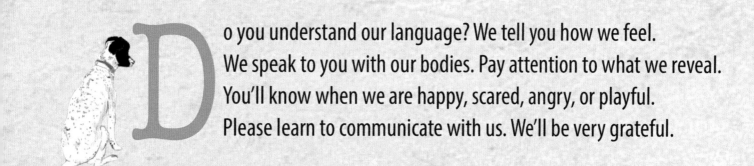

Do you understand our language? We tell you how we feel.
We speak to you with our bodies. Pay attention to what we reveal.
You'll know when we are happy, scared, angry, or playful.
Please learn to communicate with us. We'll be very grateful.

We need to learn to walk on a leash. Daily walks are a must.
We need to learn a better recall. We need to earn the trust.
Dog parks can be dangerous. There is often not enough space.
There are many uncontrolled dogs. Too many dogs in our face.

I like to meet with my siblings. We all landed in great places.
We get together once a year. We meet in different spaces.
We run around and play. Some of us like to swim.
Thanks to people like you, our future is no longer grim.

I love to play with my parents. In fact, my favorite game
Is to look for treats hidden by my Mom that I will find and claim.
I love to spend time with my Dad. He holds a bone for me to chew.
I also love to wrestle with him and run after a ball he threw.

I can continue to tell more stories if you allow.
But I am sure that you understand my message now.
I am happy you are interested and you ask, "How can I help you?"
Please support us to ease what other dogs go through.

Cheer for us underdogs. Thank you in advance!
You cannot change our past. But you can help us have a chance.
Rescue dogs are not broken. We are experienced and wise.
Be our advocate! It will feel good. You will be surprised.

My name is Sofie. I am a pure mutt.
I don't have pedigree. I am not a pure breed; so what!
I am spunky and loyal; I have a lot of zest.
My friends' gloomy fate has inspired my quest:

No matter how old you are, let's unite!
We need to support fairness, respect and the underdog fight.

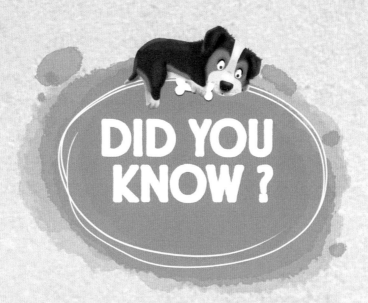

DID YOU KNOW ?

The "Canine Good Citizenship" training program focuses on basics of good manners and obedience, instilling the values of responsible ownership, and strengthening the bond between the owner and the dog at home and out in the community.

Service dogs trained to perform tasks for individuals with disabilities. Animal-assisted therapy involves therapy dogs as a form of treatment. Medically prescribed emotional support dogs provide therapeutic benefits through dedicated companionships.

Dog agility is a sport where a dog is directed through a pre-set obstacle course within a certain time limit. Obstacles can include tunnels, weave poles, tire jumps, seesaws, and pause tables where the dog must stop for a set amount of time.

I pledge to advocate for the underdog

Sign your name here

Sofie

Resources

You can find more information about shelter pets at these websites:
  * ASPCA:

     https://www.aspca.org/animal-homelessness/shelter-intake-and-surrender/
  * Petpedia:

     https://petpedia.co/animal-abuse-statistics/

     https://petpedia.co/animal-shelter-statistics/
  * Humane Society:

     https://www.humanesociety.org/resources/top-reasons-adopt-pet

You can learn more about Pit Bulls at these websites:

     https://kenneltocouch.org/2019/08/pit-bull-euthanasia-and-how-to-put-an-end-to-it/

     https://dogtime.com/dog-health/general/1220-american-pit-bull-terrier-temperament-dog-bites

You can learn more about the Canine Good Citizen Test at this website:

     https://www.akc.org/products-services/training-programs/canine-good-citizen/

You can learn more about Service Dogs, Therapy Dogs, and Emotional Support Dogs at this website:

     https://www.akc.org/expert-advice/lifestyle/service-working-therapy-emotional-support-dogs/

You can learn more about Dog Agility at this website:

     https://www.akc.org/expert-advice/training/agility-training-tips-competition/

Sofie and her siblings, like many rescue dogs in the US, were born in the South. Thanks to rescue organizations, they were saved and adopted to homes in the Northeast. When Alexandra and her husband felt they could finally offer a dog sufficient time and attention, they adopted Sofie. She has transformed their lives.

Alexandra Bach-Weidmuller grew up in a family of teachers in Germany. Books and education were firm cornerstones of her upbringing, as was a love for animals. From an early age, she was drawn to caring for pets; any pets, including dogs, cats, fish, turtles and tadpoles. She loved growing up with her dog sister, a Dalmatian named Astra.

Alexandra has volunteered in dog rescue for 15 years. She has seen firsthand what overfilled shelters and euthanasia look like. She is a coordinator with Last Hope K9 Rescue, a Boston organization that has saved over 10,000 lives since its inception in 2012.

Made in the USA
Middletown, DE
25 May 2021